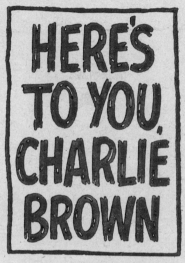

HERE'S TO YOU, CHARLIE BROWN

Selected Cartoons
from YOU CAN'T WIN,
CHARLIE BROWN VOL II

by **CHARLES M. SCHULZ**

A FAWCETT CREST BOOK
Fawcett Publications, Inc., Greenwich, Conn.

This book, prepared especially for Fawcett Publications, Inc., comprises the second half of *YOU CAN'T WIN, CHARLIE BROWN*, and is reprinted by arrangement with Holt, Rinehart and Winston, Inc.

Published by Fawcett World Library
67 West 44th Street, New York, N.Y. 10036
Printed in the United States of America

HA HA HA LOOK AT THIS IN TODAY'S PAPER...

SOME BLOCKHEAD HAS RUN AN AD IN THE "SITUATIONS WANTED" COLUMN TO GET A JOB AS MANAGER OF A BALL CLUB!

HA HA HA HA HA HA

WELL, I GUESS IT TAKES ALL KINDS TO MAKE A WORLD...

SOME KINDS WE COULD DO WITHOUT!

ANY RESPONSES TO OUR AD YET, CHARLIE BROWN?

NO, I HAVEN'T HEARD A THING...

WELL, IT'S A LITTLE EARLY YET... I'M SURE SOMEBODY WILL OFFER YOU A JOB AS MANAGER, THOUGH...

I MEAN, THERE **MUST** BE A TEAM **SOMEPLACE** THAT IS **SO** DEEP IN LAST PLACE, AND IS **SO** PANIC STRICKEN THAT IT'S WILLING TO TRY **ANYTHING!**

I DIDN'T PUT THAT VERY WELL, DID I?

NO, YOU DIDN'T!

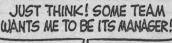

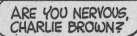

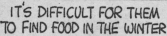

I THINK I'M AHEAD OF MY TIME...

HA! THAT'S A LAUGH! YOU'RE JUST LIKE A LOT OF OTHERS WHO SAY THE SAME THING! IT'S AN EXCUSE, THAT'S WHAT IT IS!

IT'S AN EXCUSE FOR YOUR OWN LACK OF REAL TALENT AND ABILITY!!!

I WAS SUPPOSED TO MEET CHARLIE BROWN HERE AT TWO O'CLOCK, BUT I THINK I'M AHEAD OF MY TIME..

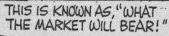

MY DAD HATES ME...

MONDAY NIGHT HE WENT TO A PTA MEETING, TUESDAY NIGHT IT WAS THE SCHOOL BOARD, WEDNESDAY NIGHT IT WAS THE BOARD OF DEACONS AND LAST NIGHT IT WAS BOWLING!

SO THIS MORNING HE SAYS TO ME, "HI, THERE!" AND I SAID, "WHO ARE YOU? I DON'T RECOGNIZE YOU!"

HE DOESN'T ACTUALLY HATE ME... HE JUST THINKS I'M TOO SARCASTIC!

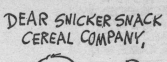

DEAR SNICKER SNACK
CEREAL COMPANY,

I APPRECIATE YOUR OFFER
OF ONE HUNDRED
REVOLUTIONARY WAR SOLD-
IERS FOR FIFTEEN CENTS.

HOWEVER, BEING AGAINST
VIOLENCE, I AM NOT
SURE I WANT THEM.

INSTEAD, COULD I PLEASE
HAVE A SET OF
PEACE-TIME CIVILIANS?

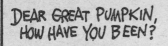

YOU'RE AT IT AGAIN, AREN'T YOU?

"THE GREAT PUMPKIN RISES OUT OF THE PUMPKIN PATCH ON HALLOWEEN NIGHT, AND FLIES THROUGH THE AIR!" GOOD GRIEF!

HOW CAN YOU **BELIEVE** THAT?

I **HAVE** TO BELIEVE IT...I'VE ALREADY SENT OUT FIFTY-SEVEN PUMPKIN CARDS...

IT WOULD BE ECONOMICALLY DISASTROUS FOR ME **NOT** TO BELIEVE IT!

ISN'T LINUS GOING OUT FOR "TRICKS OR TREATS"?

NO, HE'S SITTING IN THE PUMPKIN PATCH WAITING FOR THE GREAT PUMPKIN TO APPEAR

WELL, WHEN YOU GO UP TO THIS NEXT HOUSE, ASK THE LADY FOR AN EXTRA TREAT FOR YOUR LITTLE BROTHER WHO IS SITTING OUT IN THE PUMPKIN PATCH

ALL I GOT FROM HER WAS A VERY PECULIAR LOOK!

I THOUGHT I TOLD YOU TO LEAVE MY COMIC BOOKS ALONE?!

CAN'T YOU REMEMBER ANYTHING YOU'RE TOLD? WHAT'S THE MATTER WITH YOU? LEAVE MY THINGS ALONE!!

I DON'T KNOW WHY YOU CAN'T REMEMBER THAT!

MAYBE ITS BECAUSE I'M GETTING OLDER...MY MIND DOESN'T RETAIN THINGS LIKE IT USED TO!

IT WAS NICE OF THEM TO ASK ME, BUT I JUST HAD TO SAY, "NO"

I SUPPOSE BECAUSE THEY USE MY PLACE FOR THEIR MEETINGS THEY FELT OBLIGATED TO ASK ME TO JOIN THEIR GROUP

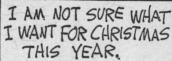

ONE LAST FLING!

WHAT ARE **YOU** GOING TO GET ME FOR BEETHOVEN'S BIRTHDAY, CHARLIE BROWN?

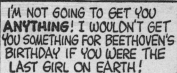

I'M NOT GOING TO GET YOU **ANYTHING!** I WOULDN'T GET YOU SOMETHING FOR BEETHOVEN'S BIRTHDAY IF YOU WERE THE LAST GIRL ON EARTH!

WHAT HAVE YOU GOT AGAINST BEETHOVEN?

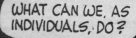

DO YOU THINK CHARLIE BROWN REALLY COULD GET NOMINATED FOR PRESIDENT?

WHAT DO YOU MEAN, NOMINATED? DON'T YOU KNOW **ANYTHING**?

FIRST YOU HAVE TO BECOME A **PRINCE**.... **THEN** YOU GET TO BE PRESIDENT!!

IT'S FRIGHTENING WHEN I REALIZE HOW LITTLE I REALLY KNOW ABOUT GOVERNMENTAL AFFAIRS!

YOU'LL HAVE TO EXCUSE ME, FRIEDA...APPARENTLY IT'S SOMEBODY'S SUPPERTIME!

IF YOU THINK THOSE ARE FUNNY FACES YOU'RE MAKING, THEN YOU'RE SADLY MISTAKEN!

NOBODY APPRECIATES GOOD HUMOR ANY MORE

I CAN'T REMEMBER EVER HAVING A THEORY EXPLODED QUITE SO FAST!

I REALLY THINK YOU SHOULD BE ASHAMED OF YOURSELF!

·NO DOG SHOULD EVER WASTE HIS TIME SLEEPING WHEN HE COULD BE OUT CHASING RABBITS!

I DON'T KNOW... SOME OF US ARE BORN DOGS, AND SOME OF US ARE BORN RABBITS...

WHEN THE CHIPS ARE DOWN, I'LL HAVE TO ADMIT THAT MY SYMPATHY LIES WITH THE RABBITS

YOU STOP SCOWLING AT ME LIKE THAT!

YOU'RE **STILL** SCOWLING AT ME..

YOU'RE SCOWLING AT ME **INSIDE**! STOP SCOWLING AT ME INSIDE!

RATS! IF YOU CAN'T EVEN SCOWL **INSIDE** WHAT IS THERE LEFT?

I'VE DECIDED WE NEED A BASEBALL SCOUT!

WE NEED SOMEONE TO GO OVER, AND MINGLE WITH THE OTHER TEAM, AND FIND OUT THEIR STRENGTH AND WEAKNESSES..

IT CAN BE A VERY DANGEROUS JOB, OF COURSE, BUT IT'S A JOB THAT NEEDS TO BE DONE, AND...

I'VE FOUND YOU A VOLUNTEER!

ALL RIGHT, SO I'M A BASEBALL SCOUT...WHAT DO I DO?

YOU GO, AND FIND OUT ALL YOU CAN ABOUT THEIR PITCHERS AND HITTERS..

WRITE EVERYTHING YOU FIND OUT ON THIS SQUARE OF BUBBLE GUM..IF THEY SUSPECT THAT YOU'RE SCOUTING THEM, YOU CAN JUST CHEW UP THE EVIDENCE...

WELL, GOOD LUCK, OL' BUDDY...

THANK YOU, CHARLIE BROWN..

SOMEHOW I HAVE THE FEELING OF IMPENDING DOOM!

MAYBE I SHOULDN'T HAVE SENT LINUS OUT AS A BASEBALL SCOUT...

MAYBE HE'LL GET LOST..MAYBE THE OTHER TEAM WILL SEE WHAT HE'S DOING, AND BEAT HIM UP...

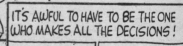

HEY, MANAGER, DO YOU THINK MY HAIR LOOKS ALL RIGHT THIS WAY, OR SHOULD I CHANGE IT?

NO, IT LOOKS FINE JUST THE WAY IT IS.

IT'S AWFUL TO HAVE TO BE THE ONE WHO MAKES ALL THE DECISIONS!

I'M SORRY THAT YOU HAVE TO WEAR GLASSES, LINUS...

DON'T FEEL SORRY FOR ME, CHARLIE BROWN...WHY, I CAN SEE THINGS NOW THAT I NEVER KNEW EVEN EXISTED BEFORE!

TAKE LUCY FOR INSTANCE...FOR THE FIRST TIME I REALIZE WHAT A GORGEOUS CREATURE SHE REALLY IS!

GLASSES HAVEN'T IMPROVED ONLY HIS SIGHT...THEY'VE ALSO IMPROVED HIS SARCASM!

NOT AGAIN?

YES, AND I CAN'T FIND THEM ANYWHERE!

WELL, IF YOU'RE GOING TO WEAR GLASSES, YOU'RE GOING TO HAVE TO LEARN TO HANG ON TO THEM!

"GENTLEMEN, I'D LIKE TO PRESENT TO YOU THE NEW CHAIRMAN OF THE BOARD!"

GOOD GRIEF! DON'T YOU HAVE ANY PATIENCE AT ALL?!!

THE SNICKER SNACK CEREAL COMPANY SPENT FORTY THOUSAND DOLLARS TO DEVELOP A BOX TOP THAT CAN BE OPENED EASILY, AND YOU RIP THE WHOLE TOP CLEAN OFF!!

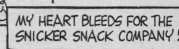

MY HEART BLEEDS FOR THE SNICKER SNACK COMPANY!

ZOOM

WITH A LITTLE PRACTICE
I BET I COULD GET THE
SHOES, TOO!

HOW COULD YOU FORGET BEETHOVEN'S BIRTHDAY?

YOU, OF ALL PEOPLE! IT WOULD BE DIFFERENT IF IT WERE SOMEONE ELSE...

BUT YOU! YOU'RE THE ONE WHO'S THE NUT ON BEETHOVEN!!

YOU HAVE A WAY OF PUTTING THINGS SO NICELY..

OF COURSE, I REALIZE THAT THERE WILL ALWAYS BE CRITICISM..

ALL MEDIUMS OF ENTERTAINMENT GO THROUGH THIS..EVEN OUR HIGHER ART FORMS HAVE THEIR DETRACTORS...THE THEATRE SEEMS ESPECIALLY VULNERABLE..

AND GOODNESS KNOWS HOW MUCH CRITICISM IS LEVELED AT OUR TELEVISION PROGRAMMING..ONE SOMETIMES WONDERS IF IT IS POSSIBLE EVER TO PLEASE THE VAST MAJORITY OF PEOPLE...

THE MOST RECENT CRITICISM IS THAT THERE IS TOO LITTLE ACTION AND FAR TOO MUCH TALKING IN THE MODERN-DAY COMIC STRIP... WHAT DO YOU THINK ABOUT THIS?

RIDICULOUS!

YOU KNOW, IT'S VERY STRANGE...

WHEN I FIRST GOT MY GLASSES, THEY KIND OF BOTHERED ME...

I GUESS I JUST WASN'T USED TO THEM..

NOW, I'M SOMETIMES NOT EVEN AWARE I HAVE THEM ON!

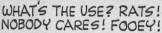

HAPPINESS IS FEELING THE WIND AND THE RAIN IN YOUR HAIR!

SORT OF!